Greta and the Labrador

Greta and the Labrador

By

Kevin Jackson

Illustrated by

Jo Dalton

www.hhousebooks.com

ISBN: 978-1-910688-59-5
Cover design by Jo Dalton
Typeset by Jo Dalton
Published in the UK
Holland House Books
47 Greenham Road
Newbury, Berkshire
RG14 7HY
UK
www.hhousebooks.com

For Dr Evie Johnson and Prof. Glyn Johnson

"Say my glory was I had such friends"

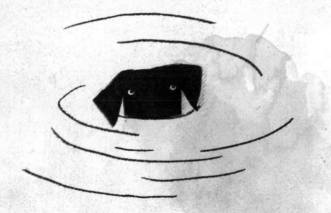

"Miss Garbo sounds a really sympathetic woman!
The poor soul I feel for her"

—*T.E. Lawrence.*

FITT THE FIRST

Miss Greta Garbo was her name

And no one rivalled her for fame.

Her beauty was beyond compare –

Her gleaming skin, her lustrous hair,

Her eyes, which seemed about to weep,

Her lips, which kept young lads from sleep,

Her noble brow, her marble cheek,

Her chin, which made strong men go weak...

And yet it was not one sole feature

Which made her such a glorious creature:

The whole was greater than its parts.

She ravished countless aching hearts.

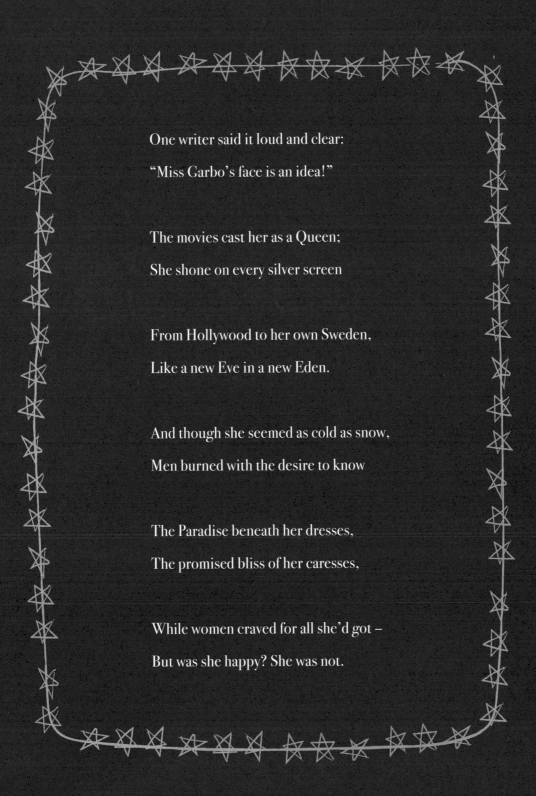

One writer said it loud and clear:

"Miss Garbo's face is an idea!"

The movies cast her as a Queen;

She shone on every silver screen

From Hollywood to her own Sweden,

Like a new Eve in a new Eden.

And though she seemed as cold as snow,

Men burned with the desire to know

The Paradise beneath her dresses,

The promised bliss of her caresses,

While women craved for all she'd got –

But was she happy? She was not.

No human form gave her delight;

She'd howl with rage through each long night

And all day long she'd sit and moan:

"I simply want to be alone!"

The movie-men were all distraught

To see the Swedish Swan they'd caught

Now slumped down on her plaster throne

Demanding to be left alone.

So, seeing how she wept and sighed,
They gathered round her and all cried:

"Just tell us how we can atone?"
"You fools, I want to be alone!"

"All right, so maybe we'll postpone..."
"Get lost! I want to be alone!"

She craved it as a dog a bone.

Her only wish: to be alone.

The movie men were wracked with woe:

They knew they'd have to let her go.

And so she fled the Pleasure Dome

Of Hollywood, and went back home.

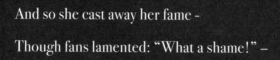

And so she cast away her fame -

Though fans lamented: "What a shame!" –

Flew to the town where she was born,

And felt a little less forlorn.

But not for long. Her lovely face

Was dear to all the Swedish race

And every day, some smiling Swede

(Not knowing of her burning need

For quiet) would stop her in the street

And say "How wonderful to meet

The loveliest woman in the world!"

She was not pleased; she simply whirled

Around and fled back to her flat.

No peace in Stockholm. That was that.

Once more she packed up, and set forth

To find a home in Sweden's North,

Where none would recognise her beauty –

Or know, at least, it was their duty

Not to pester her with queries

Or tell her all their silly theories

Of what "Ninotchka" really meant.

Such movie-chatter always sent

Poor Greta into howling rage.

She's heard enough to last an age...

So Greta found a rural house

And settled there. No need to grouse

About the locals – they were farmers,

Good solid folk, not like the "charmers"

And creeps who'd made her life a Hell

In Hollywood. Now, she felt well.

But peace can't last. Some months went by

And one by one, the folks would try

To be her friends. They bought her dishes

Piled high with grub; alas, her wishes

For peace and quiet were wholly doomed.

At night, she dreamed she was entombed,

And wept when she woke up alive.

She saw that she could never thrive

While kindly souls would bring her food

And ask if everything were good?

Then one day came the final straw.

She heard a scratching at the door.

She opened up, and there she found

A mangy-looking, old black hound.

A Labrador, to be exact.

A sorry sight, and that's a fact.

His coat was matted, caked with mud,

His paws were red from his own blood,

His eyes were dim, his body thin.

He whimpered: "Won't you let me in?"

But Greta's heart was ice and fog:

"Leave me alone, you naughty dog!"

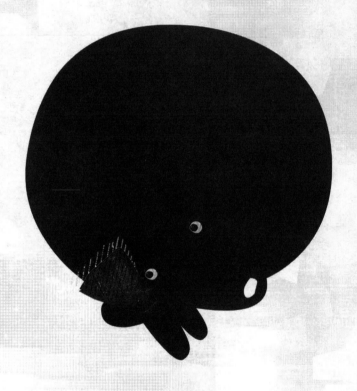

She was not moved. She slammed the door

And cursed this pesky Labrador.

The night soon came, and with it snow.

The dog curled up. He would not go.

He hoped the Lady would be kind.

He hoped that she would change her mind.

Perhaps she would give him a bone,

This goddess who lived here alone?

FITT THE THIRD

That night Miss Garbo could not sleep.

She tried and tried, but could not keep

Her mind from toying with wild plans.

What place on earth was free from man's

Repulsive face? (And woman's, too.)

Where could she go? What should she do?

But as dawn broke the answer came.

The land where no one knew her name

Was right on top of the whole world.

She smiled at last, and snugly curled

Up in her sheets. She knew her goal.

Garbo would go to the North Pole.

She fell asleep, and dreamed till noon.

She roused herself, and then, quite soon

She dressed, and gulped a coffee down,

And set off for the nearest town,

Where she would buy a one-way ticket

To the deep north. Her wooden picket

Fence was almost swamped in snow.

Its gate hung open, and, below

Its wooden bars was a strange lump
Of thick-packed flakes – it made her jump!

She prayed that it was just a rock...
She felt her cheeks go cold with shock.

Surely, that doggie must have known
Better than to stay there all alone?

For surely the most stubborn hound
Would not have hugged the icy ground

And let his warm life ebb away,
Never to bark another day?

So Greta ran. With heaving breast
She scraped snow from her doggie guest.

He was quite still, but not quite stiff.

She made a swift decision. If

She brought this canine back inside,

And wrapped him up, and really tried

To snatch him from the jaws of death...

And yet she saw no signs of breath.

She pushed and pulled the frozen form

Inside; then set him down to warm

By her wood stove. She took a towel

And briskly rubbed him. Not a growl

Or whimper came from the poor dog.

She paused, and threw another log

Into the stove, and rubbed again.

She rubbed with all her might and main.

And yet, however hard she'd try

He would not open up an eye.

The world thought Garbo was aloof,

But now she prayed for one quiet "Woof!"

She gave up, and caressed his head.

The dog was obviously dead.

But then: how wonderful! How grand!

She felt a rough tongue lick her hand!

And icy Greta wept for joy.

"Hello again, you silly boy!"

FITT THE FOURTH

Now that the dog was back to life,

The actress played the role of wife:

She gave him water, cooked him stews,

Washed his paws, and let him choose

His place to sleep, or lightly nap

(He would have crawled into her lap,

But was too shy.) She'd comb his fur,

And it came as a surprise to her –

She liked to pat his warm, smooth head.

And when she went upstairs to bed

She felt herself inclined to cry:

"Come on, then, silly! Beddie-bye!"

But no: her bed was like a throne,

Designed for her and her alone.

Instead, she'd merely say "Good-night!",

And went upstairs – but left one light

So that the lab would not be scared:

And this was the routine they shared.

In his own way, the dog reflected:

"How nice it is to be protected!"

Contented, he began to snooze:

He'd found his true love and his muse.

"She is my mistress and my saviour –

I must show her my best behaviour!"

And when she came back from above

His eyes were all ablaze with love.

Day followed day. The dog grew strong,

So Greta let him come along

When she went out to take her walk.

The villagers began to talk –

How odd to see their lovely hermit

So tolerant that she would permit

A mangy hound to frisk and leap

Around her heels, while she would keep

Quite strictly to her usual path.

Some gossiped, while their friends would laugh.

Had their Ice Queen begun to melt?

They watched her stroke her pooch's pelt.

She never once had shown affection,

Yet now, it seemed, her cold perfection

Had finally begun to crack.

And Greta? Her thoughts wandered back

To Hollywood, and misery.

Things now felt different; could it be

That the pure love this dog had shown

Could sooth her ache to be alone?

Two weeks went past. Her mind returned

To Polar zones. Oh, how she burned

To live away from human prattle!

She'd sell her Swedish goods and chattels

And book a passage on a ship.

Alas, no place on such a trip

For her new pal. For though it pained

Her just a bit, she still remained

Determined to escape mankind.

She'd set him loose – quite soon he'd find

Another warm and loving home;

A mistress who, like her, would comb

His fur (now sleek) and throw him sticks.

No backward glances, then; she'd fix

Her eyes on her Arctic ambition;

No sentiment should thwart that mission.

One afternoon, she called a car

And told the driver to go far

And deep into the local woods,

Then set the dog free - no good

For him to whimper, howl or bark.

"Go now!" The sky was growing dark.

She watched the taxi till it vanished,

Hardened her heart, and tried to banish

All fondness for her canine friend.

Too bad: this had to be the end.

She went indoors, and up to bed,

To rest before the trials ahead...

Out in the woods, a lone dog cries,

And howls his anguish to the skies.

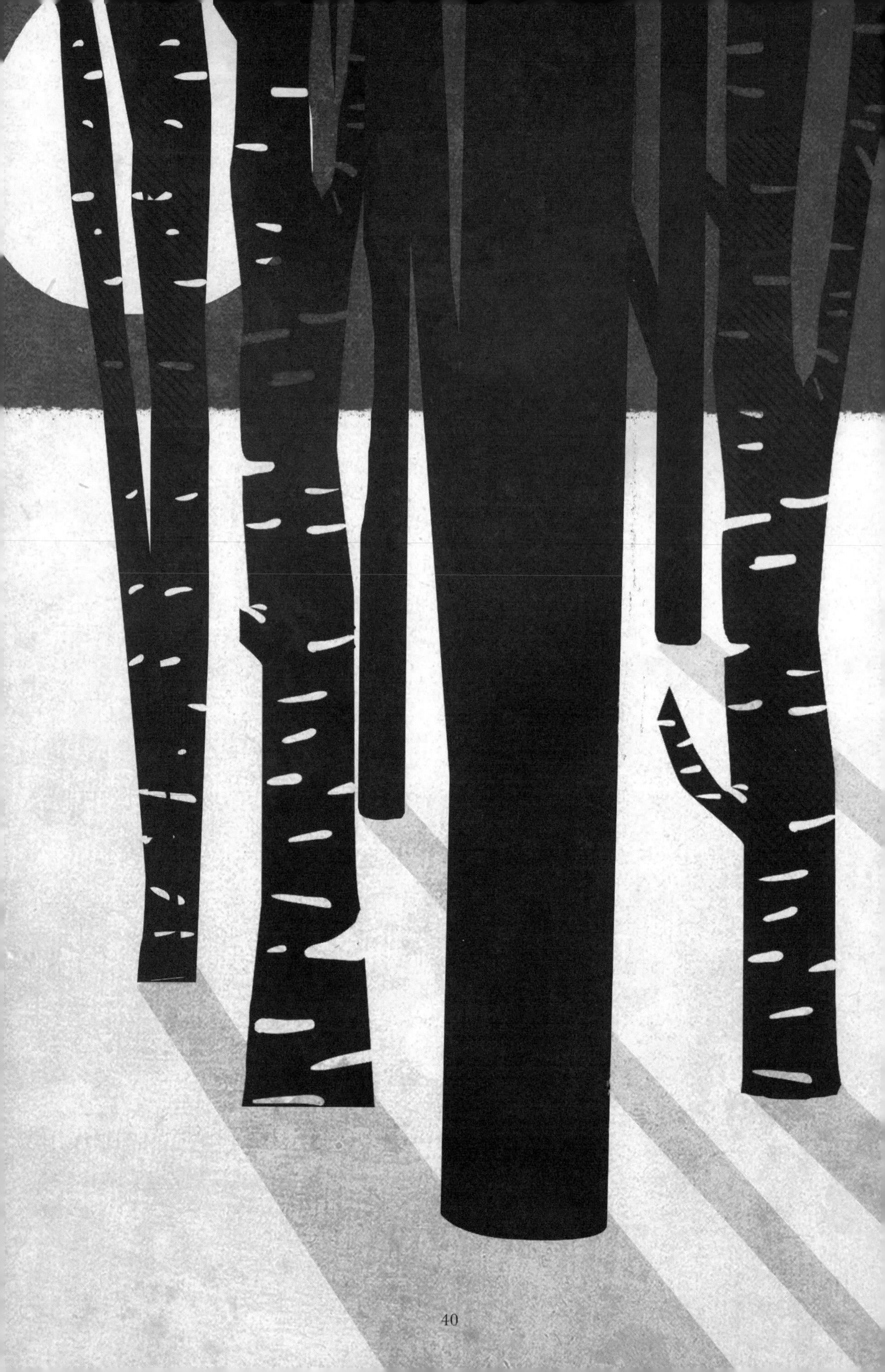

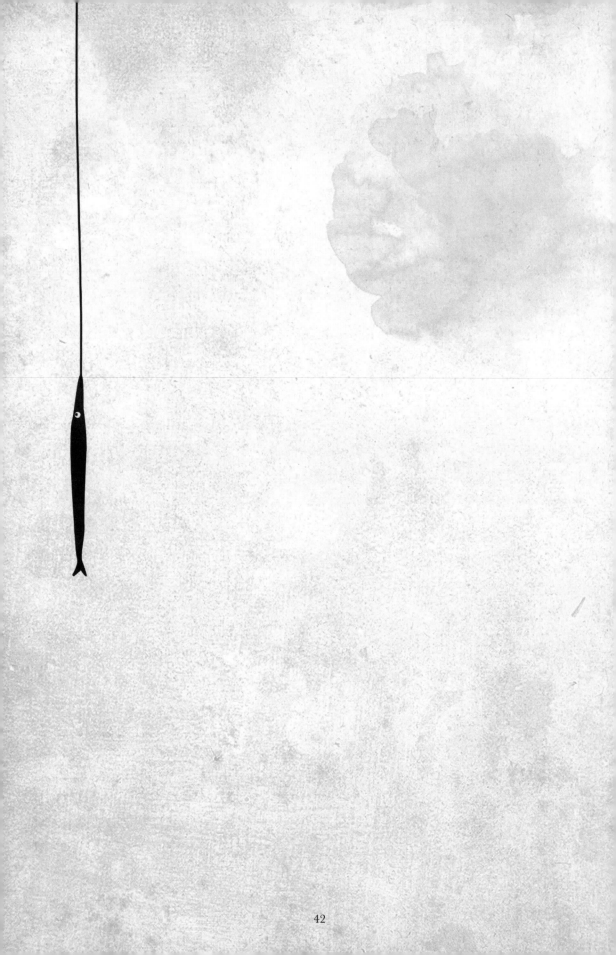

FITT THE FITH

Did Greta feel the pangs of guilt?

Well, yes, a bit; but she was built

Of sterner stuff by far than most;

Her family had been a host

Of Viking warriors and bards.

She found it easy to be hard,

And all that night she slept quite sound

And dreamed of sailing up around

The coast of Sweden to seek bliss.

Her dreams were thrilling as a kiss.

When morning broke, she went and caught

An early bus to the sea port,

To see if she could find some Jolly

Jack Tar to indulge her folly –

Some tolerant, obliging soul

To sail her up to the North Pole.

Her luck was good: with a minute

She found a wooden hut; within it

Sat a fine chap with a vast beard –

A Captain! Though Greta had feared

That no Old Salt would hear her plea

This fellow smiled, and said that he

Would gladly take her to the Pole.

"No worries, Miss!" he said. His sole

Condition was: she could not sail

Alone. And then he told his tales

Of Arctic travels gone to Hell,

Of deaths and madness... He could tell

A thousand yarns of Arctic grief.

He scratched his beard. His firm belief

Was that he did not dare to send

A passenger who had no friend

For company in Polar zones.

He would not let her sail alone.

"But," Greta said, "I have no friend!"

He thought about this. In the end

He said: "OK, So here's my plan.

You need not travel with a man

Or woman; but that's no disaster.

I think that we can fix this faster

If you'll agree to this one term:

Find a good dog. I'm wholly firm

On this - see, here's my Captain's Log:

Sole passengers must bring a dog.

He'll keep you safe and warm up there,

And chase away the polar bears."

Greta was silent. Could it be

That it was now her destiny

To share her life with a canine?

The Captain noticed her eyes shine:

Though Greta was not used to chums,

She felt, deep down inside, a numb

Sensation of both loss and woe.

She would not hesitate: she'd go

Straight back home, and if she could,

Track down her dog in the dark wood.

But back home much to her surprise! –

She saw a pair of liquid eyes.

The Labrador! Some doggy sense

Had brought him right back to her fence!

He did not know what she would do:

For, in his canine mind, he knew

That she had spurned his love... but now!

She patted him upon his brow,

Caressed his ears, and rubbed his legs.

He jumped and rolled and frisked and begged,

And danced around her, mad with joy.

"It's good to see you, silly boy!

Let's get you warm and dry." And then

She led him back inside; and when

He was quite warm, she hugged him tight

And stayed with him all that long night.

They cuddled up on the bare floor

Greta and her Labrador.

FITT THE SIXTH

The next days went by in a flash

As Greta laid out piles of cash

For all the things they'd surely need.

She bought a suit of Harris Tweed,

Thick boots for walking on the ice,

And thicker books, full of advice

On how to thrive in deadly cold:

'A Starter's Guide to Igloos' told

How she could build a cosy home

From blocks of ice; another tome

Explained how best to hunt and fish

In Arctic climes. Her dearest wish,

For solitude, was coming true.

(Of course, she'd take her doggie, too.)

She also shopped for good strong rope,

And bully beef, and bars of soap,

Knives, harpoons, sponges, lamps and oil,

A fish-kettle, in which to boil

The sprats she'd catch through little holes –

No need to starve at the North Pole!

And last, she blew her final wedge

On a fast-running, lightweight sledge:

Her Labrador was clearly bright –

He'd learn to pull this sledge, all right!

Soon it was time to leave, so she

Took all her kit down to the quay.

The Captain's greeting was quite hearty –

As if their voyage would be a party.

He took down a quick inventory

Of all her goods, and heard the story

Of how the Lab became her chum.

He laughed and said, "All right, then come

On board the ship – Oh, one last thing.

Since you'd decided that you'll bring

That dog along – He looks quite tame! –

I really need to know his name

So I can keep our records straight."

Silence. Would he have to wait

Forever for her answer? Yes,

It seemed so. He could only guess

Why lovely Greta would not speak.

A minute passed. And then a weak

Smile floated across Greta's face.

Sure, why not make this dock the place

Where she would give her dog a name?

It would, let's face it, be a shame

For her sweet pooch to stay "Anon."

It was as if she'd somehow gone

Into a trance. And then she said:

"Pikus." And patted her dog's head.

A shudder ran through her dog's frame –

At last! He had his own true name!

The Captain smiled. "A splendid choice –

Now step on board, before we hoist

The anchor high and leave this port."

So Greta and her male escort

Climbed up the gang-plank eagerly.

In half an hour they were at sea.

The waves were calm, the sun was high,

Seagulls played across the sky.

Greta and Pikus, side by side

Watched the white birds as they would glide

About the ship, in search of food.

Pikus and Greta felt how good

It was to voyage. They would stay

Up on the fore-deck all that day,

And gaze back at the distant shore,

Greta and her Labrador.

FITT THE SEVENTH

Their ship was called the *Arctic Crow*,

A merchant vessel, which would go

On frequent trips along the coast

Of Norway – well, that was the most

Familiar journey – bearing cargo

(Just like the days of Wells and Fargo

In the Wild West) for quick sales

In Murmansk or Archangel. Whales

Would swim beside her, frisking.

But this time out the *Crow* was risking

Colder waters, just for Greta,

Who stood on deck in her thick sweater,

And stared. Her eyes were even keener

Than in that shot from *Queen Christina*

In which the royal lady stands

On a ship's prow. Her gloveless hands

Would sometimes give her dog a pat –

He gazed up at her, happy that

He'd found his true mistress at last.

His miseries were in the past:

He'd stay with her no matter what,

And give her all the love he'd got.

Their luck was good. That week the weather

Was fairly mild; and so, together,

Greta and Pikus trod the decks,

Felt the sea spray, and craned their necks

To see if they could spot some seals,

Or dolphins, sharks or giant eels...

Or the Lofoten Islands, where

The captain told his mate to bear

Due North. This was a real surprise –

The crew had not been told. Loud cries

Of "What's all this?" now rent the air.

The skipper calmed them. "Lads, fair's fair.

Each one of you gets triple pay!

Just trust me boys – you'll bless the day

You men have signed on for the *Crow*

Now all we have to do is go

As far as the first Polar ice.

We drop Miss Garbo off, all nice

And gently, then it's back to normal."

The crew fell silent. True, no formal

Contract held them to this task –

But: triple pay? They could not ask

For better terms. They soon agreed

To push ahead – don't call it greed,

Just a strong sense of their true worth.

That night, tucked up inside her berth

With Pikus at her feet, our Greta

Mused that it had all gone much better

Than she had feared. And soon, ahead,

Was the North Pole. She let her head

Sink deep into her fluffy pillow.

Outside, the waves were merely billows.

Pikus watched her as she slept,

And like all loyal dogs, he kept

His eyes awake all through the night.

This was no chore, but pure delight.

The *Crow* sailed on. Her sturdy crew

Would moan about the cold, but knew

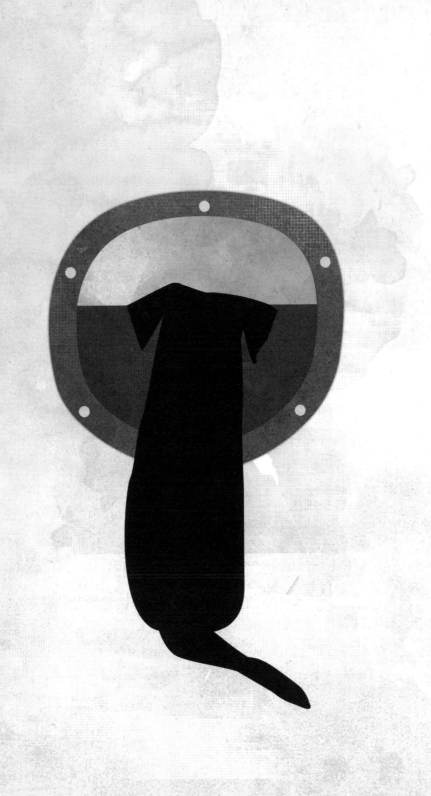

And right up to the Northern Pole –

Just at the iron whim of one sole

Passenger (plus dog). What larks!

They'd play with Pikus, and his barks

Rang merrily about the ship.

The air grew colder; soon, the trip

Would be successfully completed.

Morale was good – the crew competed

To see if one of them could thaw

Their "Pole Star" with a witty joke, or

Somehow make her laugh. No dice.

She laughed with Pikus, but stayed ice

With all the jolly sailor boys.

Then, finally, one day: "Ahoy!"

The call rang out. "Pack ice ahead!"

She ran out from her soft warm bed

With Pikus at her heels. She gasped.

Ahead of them there lay a vast

And dazzling expanse of ice.

To Greta, this was Paradise.

They gazed and gazed in silent awe,

Greta and her Labrador.

FITT THE LAST

The *Crow* now touched the ice's edge.

The crewman lowered Greta's sledge

And placed it safely on the ice.

The Captain gave some last advice:

"Miss Garbo, take the greatest care –

There's danger here from Polar bears!

Just radio if you need help –

It seems to me that your black whelp's

Not company enough for you…"

But Greta stopped him: "That will do!

My Pikus is a splendid hound,

With him I shall be safe and sound!

Now tell your sailors to unload

My things!" And so the crewmen rowed

Their rowboats, and they brought ashore

The rest of all Miss Garbo's store

Of food and fuel and useful kit.

The work took several hours, but it

Was still quite light when they had done.

(This is a land of midnight sun.)

The sledge was loaded, and, at last

They strapped brave Pikus good and fast

Into his harness – gave a push

(While Greta gaily shouted "Mush!")

And set the sledge speeding away.

She gave a wave, as if to say:

"This is goodbye, not au revoir!"

They watched her speed away, so far

That she could not be seen. "What folly!"

They muttered. Ha! She would be jolly

Lucky to survive a year –

Or even weeks. Yes, it was clear

That Greta's was an insane trip.

They shrugged, and went back to the ship.

Now Pikus, strapped into his traces

Felt like a greyhound at the races;

He pulled the sledge with all his might,

While Greta laughed from sheer delight.

They'd stop at times, to pitch a tent

To rest a while, and then they went

Right to our planet's very top.

She checked her compass, and said: "Stop!"

They had arrived. It was the Pole!

Pure happiness suffused her soul;

And Pikus, sensing how she felt

Was happy too. The sight would melt

The hardest heart: actress and hound

Had overcome the odds, and found

A land where they could be content.

One final time she pitched the tent.

Tomorrow she would start to build

A house of ice, sturdy and filled

With all the kit she'd brought along.

And as she built, she sang a song

From her young days – a charming ditty.

Her dog stayed quiet – what a pity

He'd never learned to sing in tune!

Greta worked fast, and very soon

She's built herself a fine igloo –

A des. res. with a Southern view

From every side! And then she took

Her stores, and filled up every nook

With furniture and suchlike stuff:

A table, chairs and a good tough

Canvas to put upon the floor,

Plus lamps and stoves and much much more,

Within ice walls they're warm and snug.

The Labrador sleeps on his rug,

While Greta has her cosy bed

With counterpane of white and red.

They have adventures every day,

She fishes, then they both will play

At snowballs, slides and other games.

She calls her Pikus silly names.

At night they eat a meal of fish

(The Labrador has his own dish)

And listen to the gramophone.

"How glad I am to be alone!"

She thinks, "... with just my Labrador.
It's everything that I hoped for!"

And so we reach our happy end,
Miss Garbo has a special friend

And they'll stay friends for ever more,
Greta and her Labrador.

AFTERWORD

The real-life Greta Garbo, who bears only occasional resemblances to the heroine of this poem, did in fact have a marked fondness for dogs. At one time she owned a pet Chow called Flimsy (splendid name!), and there are at least half a dozen portraits of her posing with and fussing over noble hounds in her leisure hours – mostly big ones, Dobermans and German Shepherds and other hunting dogs. One of her biographers reports that whenever she co-starred with a dog in one of her films, she would swiftly acquire one of the same breed as a pet. As Queen Christina, in the gorgeous film of that name, she is often accompanied by a brace of large, stately canines in whose company she seems very happy. As far as I know, however, she never had a Labrador for a friend.

Nor did she ever travel to the Arctic. (Though she might have found it congenial, since she was descended from Lapps – or, more correctly, Sami -- on her mother's side.) When she ran from Hollywood into self-imposed exile from the cinema in 1941, she settled not in the snowy North but in a New York apartment, where she lived a quiet life, seeing only the old friends she could trust to protect her privacy. If not quite a recluse on the Howard Hughes scale, she shunned all publicity and was tormented by the paparazzi who chased after her even in her frail old age, when she was almost unrecognizable as the greatest female star the studio system had ever produced. (And also the most highly paid.) Despite her ferocious will-power and imperious presence before the camera, she remained shy, even timid with strangers. Lawrence Olivier, who was once screen-tested for a part as her love interest, remembered that she was as "shy as an antelope".

The Garbo of *Greta and the Labrador* is, then, not really the great Swedish actress, but rather a kind of beautiful emblem for the condition of solitude -- a fantasy figure inspired in large measure by her most famous line: "I want to be alone". The film that made this line universally known was *Grand Hotel,* in which her character, the *prima ballerina* Gruskynskaya, enunciates it with vehement gloom, but she had already spoken them in a previous role, as the heroine of *The Single Standard*: "I am walking alone because I want to be alone." And this was already screenwriting imitating life. When interviewers asked her why she had never married, she usually told them: "I like to be alone, not always with the same person."

Later, she would say that she liked travelling because it allowed you to be on your own. The phrase, and the sentiment, became so strongly identified with her that she eventually sent it up in the delightful comedy *Ninotchka*, in which her character begins as a stern, puritanical representative of the Soviet Union. "Do you want to be alone, Comrade?", she is asked. "No!" is her reply. The original title for *Ninotchka* was *We Want to be Alone*.

My imaginary Greta is torn between two desires: her conscious longing to flee from humanity, and her unconscious need for love, which she eventually admits to and finds in non-human form. But why is her saviour a *black dog*? Because of the English tradition of calling states of melancholy, depression and despair "Black Dog": Samuel Johnson used this name for his own savage glooms, as did Sir Walter Scott and Sir Winston Churchill. This is a gross slander and libel on that glorious species, whose powerful anti-depressant qualities are now generally acknowledged by doctors.

In short, I wanted to write a sort of fairy story about a journey from melancholy to contentment, with an ending that might not be happy for most people, but is bliss for my heroine and her devoted friend. But saying this is to some degree a rationalization after the event. I began to write the poem when filing my annual tax return – a task which to me, as to most of the writers I know, is like something out of Dante. The task was so dull that my unconscious offered me something more agreeable to think about. The story came to me almost whole, and, as I put aside my piles of tatty receipts, the verses started to come almost unbidden. (This probably sounds a bit phoney but I swear that's the way it was.) I heard an iambic tetrameter, which seems more given to lightness and jokes than the elegant pentameter, and the game was afoot. It felt – no, really –more like taking dictation than writing.

Other elements of the poem fell into place over the next couple of days. About a week earlier, I had been re-reading Lewis Carroll's *The Hunting of the Snark*, so I knew there would need to be a sea voyage at some point. *Snark* reminded me of the traditional division of a narrative poem into Fitts; it also suggested that *Greta* should be a Quest Narrative, though the quest here is not for a living creature -- neither Snark nor Boojum -- but for a place where the heroine can finally Be Alone.

The polar wastes came from a number of sources, including, indirectly, the *Snark* itself, since one of the earliest interpretations of the poem suggested that it was a satire on arctic exploration, based on the voyage of two steam-ships, the *Alert* and the *Discovery* from Portsmouth to the far North and back, 1875-76. According to this reading, which few have accepted, the *Snark* is a symbol of the North Pole.

A more direct source was the frame narrative of Mary Shelley's *Frankenstein*, which is written by the Captain of a ship bound for the North Pole; and a still more immediate source was a magnificent poem about terrible loneliness (and other matters) - one that haunted Mary Shelley when she wrote her scientific fable: Coleridge's *Rime of the Ancient Mariner*, which imagines the very first European venture to the South Pole. There can't be any lines in English poetry so deeply awash in terror, isolation and self-loathing as

> The many men, so beautiful!
>
> And they all dead did lie.
>
> And a thousand, thousand slimy things lived on;
>
> And so did I.

A third and final source was my knowledge of some adventures at both North and South Poles had by a good friend, herself a Pole, and a fine photographer of ice and snow.

Pretty much everything else in the poem should be self-explanatory, though younger readers might like to be told that the writer mentioned in Fitt the First is Roland Barthes, who wrote an essay about The face of Garbo ("The face of Garbo is an Idea, that of Hepburn an Event.") that was fashionable in the Seventies and Eighties. And, as an astute earlier reader of the poem noticed, Pikus's sentiments were anticipated in a potent rock song, "*I Wanna Be Your Dog*", by Iggy and the Stooges.

Kevin Jackson, 25 February 2019.

ACKNOWLEDGEMENTS

For their encouragement, advice and moral support in the earliest days of this project, warm thanks to my friends Ranjit Bolt, Patricia Campbell, Peter Carpenter, Hunt Emerson, Helen J. Emsley, Mark Godowski, Shan Lancaster, Colin Minchin, Roger and Henrietta Parsons, Marzena Pogorzaly, Toby Poynder, Peter Swaab, George Szirtes and Bharat Tandon.

Thanks also to Jo Dalton for her delightful and witty illustrations, and above all to Robert Peett for adopting my stray dog.

ABOUT THE AUTHOR

Kevin Jackson has published more than thirty books, including *Constellation of Genius, Invisible Forms, Carnal, Moose* and the authorised biography of *Humphrey Jennings*.

His short films include *Exquisite Corpse, The Last of the Vostyachs, and A Masque for Doctor Dee*. He has also collaborated with the cartoonist Hunt Emerson on the *Fortean Times* comic series *Lives of the Great Occultists*, as well as an adaptation of *Dante's Inferno* and a trio of graphic novellas inspired by the thought of John Ruskin.

He is a Companion of the *Guild of St George*, a Fellow of the *Royal Society of Arts* and a Regent of the *College de Pataphysique*. *Greta and the Labrador* is his first long poem.

ABOUT THE ARTIST

Jo Dalton is an experimental Printmaker, Illustrator and Motion Designer. With a background in Graphic Design, she worked as a Motion Designer in London before moving to Bristol to start her own design studio *Room Fifty Nine (room59.co.uk)*.

The illustrations in this book were created using hand made textures and drawings combined with digital graphics.

She is currently sailing around the world on her boat *Boomerang* while designing, illustrating, painting and printmaking.

OTHER BOOKS BY KEVIN JACKSON

Schrader on Schrader & Other Writings (Faber, London & Boston, 1990; revised edition 2003)

The Humphrey Jennings Film Reader (ed.) (Carcanet, Manchester, 1993; paperback 2004)

The Oxford Book of Money (OUP, Oxford & New York, 1995)

The Risk of Being Alive (ed.) (Cambridge Quarterly, 1996)

The Language of Cinema (Carcanet UK, Routledge USA, 1998)

Invisible Forms (Picador UK 1999, St Martin's USA 2000)

A Ruskin Alphabet (Worple Press, Kent 2000)

Pyramid: Beyond Imagination (BBC Books, 2002; also translated into several languages)

Anthony Burgess: Revolutionary Sonnets (ed.) (Carcanet 2002; reissued 2017)

The Verbals: Conversations with Iain Sinclair (Worple, 2003)

Pataphysics: Definitions and Citations (co-ed.) (Atlas Press, 2003)

The Anatomy of Melancholy: Selections (ed.) (Carcanet Press, 2004)

Humphrey Jennings (Picador, 2004)

Letters of Introduction (Carcanet, 2004)

Withnail & I (British Film Institute, 2004)

Fast (Portobello, 2006)

The Pataphysical Flook (Atlas, 2007)

The Book of Hours (Duckworth, 2007)

Lawrence of Arabia (British Film Institute, 2007)

Moose (Reaktion, 2009)

Bite: A Vampire Handbook (Portobello, 2009)

Aussie Dans Le Metro: A Festschrift for John Baxter (Alces Press, 2009)

The Worlds of John Ruskin (Pallas Athene/Ruskin Foundation, 2010)

The Bleaching Stream (Atlas Press/LIP, 2011)

Constellation of Genius: 1922, Modernism Year Zero (Hutchinson UK, 2012, FSG USA 2013). Reissued in paperback as Constellation of Genius: Modernism and All That Jazz, 2013

Nosferatu (British Film Institute, 2015)

Carnal to the Point of Scandal (Pallas Athene, 2015)

Coles to Jerusalem (Pallas Athene, 2017)

Crimean Sonnets: An English Version (Worple Press, 2017)

Mayflower – The Voyage from Hell, 2013

Darwin's Odyssey, 2013

Columbus, The Accidental Hero 2014

The Queen's Pirate, Sir Francis Drake, 2016

Coles to Jerusalem, 2016

Huddled Masses, 2018

GRAPHIC NOVELS AND COMICS
(with the cartoonist Hunt Emerson)

How to be Rich (freely adapted from Ruskin's "Unto This Last") (Ruskin Foundation, 2006)

How to See (from "Modern Painters", etc) (Ruskin Foundation, 2008)

How to Work (from "The Nature of Gothic", etc. (2018)

Bloke's Progress (Ruskin Foundation, 2018)

Dante's Inferno (Knockabout, 2012)